PSHE & Citizenship
In Action

Year 2

Godfrey Hall

Editor: Rebecca Ferguson
Layout artist: Mark Walker at IFA Design, Plymouth
Illustrations: Pat Murray, Graham Cameron Illustration
Cover design: Martin Cross

First published 2004 by Folens Limited.

British Library Cataloguing in Publication Data. A catalogue record for this publication is available from the British Library.

ISBN 1 84303 632 0

Contents

Series introduction

This series has been designed to meet the needs of Key Stages 1 and 2. Prepared in conjunction with the QCA Schemes of Work for Citizenship, it also includes sections on personal, social and health education (PSHE).

Citizenship is a central issue in all schools, and a subject which is part and parcel of our everyday lives. Together with PSHE, it provides pupils with the knowledge, skills and understanding that are required for them to lead happy and confident lives.

It is also important that young people grow up to become not only responsible but also active and informed citizens.

Issues covered in this series include:
- right and wrong
- rules and laws
- fairness
- healthy living
- being part of the community
- decision making
- conflict and cooperation.

The material and ideas in these books have been designed so that they can be used:
- as part of an ongoing programme
- as a springboard for further investigation
- to support existing schemes.

There are 15 units in each book. Each unit contains three sections, each of which focuses on one issue and includes a worksheet to help carry out that task. Each unit provides:
- background information
- learning objectives
- QCA and Curriculum links
- differentiated activities
- follow-up ideas
- three worksheets.

The worksheets have been designed to be flexible and easily adapted to the local needs of schools and individual teachers. The activities have also been designed so that they are cross-curricular.

In the later books, pupils are encouraged to work more and more with outside agencies, extending their knowledge of the subject on both a global and a national level.

Many of the activities throughout the series are excellent starting points for projects within the community as well as for links with other schools.

With the development of e-mail and the Internet, pupils are not only able to communicate with others throughout the world; they are also able to carry out intensive research into areas of interest. This allows schools to build partnerships with others. Pupils also have the chance to work closely with their peers. Working with others, investigating sustainable development and developing local and national strategies are all part of this process.

Citizenship and PSHE are important elements of the curriculum because they:
- encourage pupils to take a full part in the life of the school and the community
- provide pupils with the opportunity to become responsible citizens
- link schools with others elsewhere in the world
- provide the ingredients for a healthy lifestyle
- support and promote equal opportunity and respect
- provide a focus for school-based projects
- provide a chance to work on real-life issues
- increase pupils' decision-making opportunities.

Responding to others

Background

Children need to feel involved in events outside the classroom, playground matters, assemblies and lunchtimes. They need to feel confident working in pairs or as a group. Working together gives them opportunities to develop their social skills and begin to consider other children's points of view. Games are good ways of getting children to co-operate with each other.

Learning Objectives

Activities in this unit will allow children to:
- work together in pairs or as a group
- look at different ways of responding to adults
- consider ways of working with friends.

QCA/Curriculum links: QCA Unit 1 • Worksheet 1 links with English and Mathematics • Worksheet 2 links with English and Art & Design• Worksheet 3 links with English and Art & Design

ACTIVITIES

Worksheet 1 Working together

Starting points: Play a simple game with the children such as I-Spy. Talk about how you play the game.

Main activity: The children should write out a set of simple rules for the game on the worksheet.

Simplified activity: The children should play the game on the worksheet with a partner. This could be extended to playing in groups of three or four.

Challenge: Ask the children to make up a simple game and devise a set of rules. They can then play the game with a friend.

Worksheet 2 My teacher

Starting points: Discuss why teachers are needed. What do they do?

Main activity: The children should complete the worksheet. They should then list on the back of the sheet the people a teacher works with during the day, for example, teaching assistant, head teacher, parents.

Simplified activity: The children should complete the worksheet.

Challenge: The children should complete the worksheet. Encourage them to go on to list ways in which they could help their teacher.

Worksheet 3 My friend

Starting points: Talk about how important friends are. When do the children need the help of a friend?

Main activity: The children should draw pictures of several friends and suggest some things they could do together.

Simplified activity: The children should complete the worksheet.

Challenge: Ask the children to list words that would describe a best friend, for example, kind and helpful.

Plenary

- *Talk to the children about the importance of having friends and working with them.*
- *Split the children into groups of four and give them an object such as a spoon or a pencil. Ask them to list different ways in which this item can be used.*
- *In a PE lesson, ask groups of children to find different ways of using a ball or a skipping rope.*

Working together

 **Play this game with a friend.
You will need counters and a dice.**

My teacher

My teacher's name is _____ .

_____ works at _____ School.

There are _____ children in _____ class.

My teacher

My friend

My friend is called _____.

_____ has _____ hair.

My friend is _____.

They like _____.

I like my friend because _____.

My friend

② Taking part in decision making

Background

It is important that children have the chance to take part in making decisions at all stages of their development. They need to be able to listen to other people's opinions and to consider different points of view. They should be given chances to decide what they might do in a given situation. This could be a decision made on their own or with others.

Learning Objectives

Activities in this unit will allow children to:
- develop their discussion skills
- consider possible alternatives
- understand that it is sometimes necessary to compromise.

QCA/Curriculum links: QCA Unit 1 • Worksheet 4 links with English and Art & Design • Worksheet 5 links with English, Mathematics and Music • Worksheet 6 links with English and Mathematics

ACTIVITIES

Worksheet 4 What should I do?

Starting points: Show the children a picture of a tree or river. 'What kind of accident might happen here? What could you do to help?'

Main activity: The children should add another solution for each situation and go on to complete the worksheet.

Simplified activity: The children should complete the worksheet and colour in the pictures.

Challenge: Ask the children to draw another problem and write three possible solutions beside it.

Worksheet 5 Sharing

Starting points: Sing a song about sharing such as 'Baa, baa, black sheep'. Discuss.

Main activity: The children should complete the worksheet and go on to list things that can be shared with friends.

Simplified activity: The children should complete the worksheet and colour in their answers.

Challenge: Ask the children to write a short story about something that they have shared with someone else.

Worksheet 6 The party

Starting points: Discuss what happens at a party. Ask some of the children to describe a party they have attended.

Main activity: The children should think of a number of different ways of splitting up the food and drink.

Simplified activity: The children should complete the worksheet.

Challenge: The children should consider factors that need to be looked at when dividing up the food, for example, some people might not eat sausages.

Plenary

- *Ask the children to sit in a circle. Put a teddy bear, a book and a jumper in the middle.*
- *Discuss what kind of person might like to receive each of these as a gift. Why? How have the children reached their decision?*
- *Talk about the importance of sharing things with each other.*

What should I do?

 Look at the pictures below.
Tick one answer to go with each problem.
Why did you choose that answer?

☐ jump in

☐ run for help

☐ shout

☐ cry

☐ clear it up

☐ ask a friend to clear it up

☐ get wet

☐ go and put a coat on

☐ shout for help

Sharing

Share these things between you and three friends

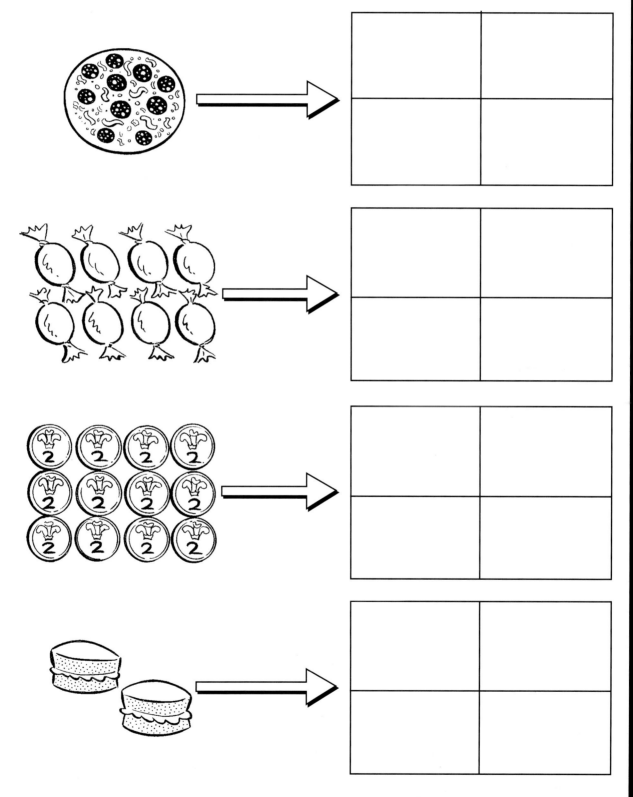

What do you like sharing with your friends?

The party

 Look at the party food and drink below.
Share it between the four friends.

Ruth

Myrna

Mehmet

Connor

③ Rules

Background

Children are not only exposed to rules inside school but also in their everyday lives outside. They need to know that rules are there to be followed. Sometimes these rules are written down but at other times they are a matter of common sense. This unit looks at a number of different situations and why rules need to be followed. The situations include swimming pool, beach and park.

Learning Objectives

Activities in this unit will allow children to:
- understand that rules are not always written down
- learn that rules need to be followed for safety reasons
- realise that rules sometimes need to be adapted to fit a situation.

QCA/Curriculum links: QCA Unit 1 • Worksheet 7 links with English and Art & Design • Worksheet 8 links with English, Design & Technology, ICT, Geography and Art & Design • Worksheet 9 links with English, Design & Technology, ICT, Geography and Art & Design

ACTIVITIES

Worksheet 7   At the swimming pool

Starting points: Show the children a picture of a swimming pool. Discuss what happens there.

Main activity: The children should complete the worksheet and then write down three more rules that should be followed at the swimming pool.

Simplified activity: The children should complete the worksheet and then list five things that can be seen in the picture.

Challenge: Ask the children to create a safety poster showing one rule that should be followed at the local swimming pool.

Worksheet 8   On the beach

Starting points: Play the game 'I went to the beach and I saw…'. Each child should add one item to the list.

Main activity: The children should use ICT to list five rules for use on the beach in the picture.

Simplified activity: The children should complete the worksheet and then discuss why these things are dangerous.

Challenge: The children should design a flag which could be flown to show when the beach is safe.

Worksheet 9   In the park

Starting points: Visit your local park. Discuss what the children like doing there.

Main activity: The children should complete the worksheet and go on to add more rules.

Simplified activity: The children should complete the worksheet.

Challenge: The children should use ICT to make a sign to go in the park showing three of the rules.

Plenary

- *Discuss with the children how rules are created. Who makes them? Talk about how some rules are written down while others are all about common sense.*
- *Make up a set of rules for some of the places the children might visit, for example, cinema, shops, doctor's surgery or river bank.*

At the swimming pool

 Tick the rules which are being broken.

☐ Do not jump in.

☐ Do not run.

☐ Do not smoke.

☐ Do not play on the edge.

☐ Do not play in the showers.

☐ Do not bring your own food and drink.

On the beach

 Circle the dangers on this beach.

In the park

 Write down five rules for people visiting this park.

(1) _____

(2) _____

(3) _____

(4) _____

(5) _____

Influences

Background

Children can be influenced by many internal and external sources. These include friends, families, advertising and their own likes and dislikes. This unit deals with ways in which they might be influenced, their own decision-making and what might change their mind.

Learning Objectives

Activities in this unit will allow children to:
- learn about different types of advert
- understand how to make choices
- understand that sometimes they may have to change their mind about something.

QCA/Curriculum links: QCA Unit 2 • Worksheet 10 links with English and Design & Technology • Worksheet 11 links with English and Mathematics • Worksheet 12 links with English, Mathematics and Art & Design

ACTIVITIES

Worksheet 10 — Adverts

Starting points: Show the children magazine adverts. Which do they like best? Why?

Main activity: The children should complete the worksheet and then draw an advert for the chocolate bar on the back of the sheet.

Simplified activity: The children should complete the worksheet.

Challenge: Ask the children to cut some more useful adjectives out of adverts in recent newspapers and magazines.

Worksheet 11 — How would I spend it?

Starting points: Ask each child to tell the others about their favourite toy.

Main activity: The children should complete the worksheet and then write down five other things they might want to buy with the money.

Simplified activity: The children should complete the worksheet.

Challenge: The children should complete the worksheet and then decide which of these things they might give to a friend as a present. Why?

Worksheet 12 — Who or what might change my mind?

Starting points: Set up a simple shop in the class and let the children take turns to use it.

Main activity: The children should complete the worksheet and then list things that might change a person's mind about buying something, for example, cost, colour or size.

Simplified activity: The children should complete the worksheet. They might draw parents, friends or shop assistants.

Challenge: The children should complete the worksheet and then discuss how an advert might change what they think of something.

Plenary

- *Talk about decisions the children might make when they go to buy something.*
- *Discuss what adverts do and how they are designed to persuade people to buy things.*
- *Ask the children to cut some of their favourite adverts from newspapers and magazines.*

Adverts

 Colour in three words to describe this chocolate bar.

bad   horrible

good

tasty   sticky

yummy smelly

delicious

Put each of these words into a sentence.

How would I spend it?

 If you were given £10 to spend, tick which of these you would buy. Why?

Who or what might change my mind?

 Draw people below who might change your mind about buying something.

Likes and dislikes

Background

There are often times when children have to make a decision. Sometimes this is on their own and sometimes it is with a friend. It is important they understand that when they have to make a decision with someone else they have to take into consideration that person's opinion. If they are making a decision on their own they may need to consider a range of factors.

Learning Objectives

Activities in this unit will allow children to:
- understand that they sometimes have to consider other people when making a decision
- understand that they may have to consider alternatives
- realise that they may have to explain their choices to others.

QCA/Curriculum links: QCA Unit 2 • Worksheet 13 links with English • Worksheet 14 links with English and Art & Design • Worksheet 15 links with English and Art & Design

ACTIVITIES

Worksheet 13 Friends

Starting points: Discuss which games the children like playing with their friends.

Main activity: The children should complete the worksheet and then write on the back why they have chosen these things.

Simplified activity: The children should complete the worksheet and draw one of the things they have chosen.

Challenge: The children should write a short story about somewhere they have visited with a friend.

Worksheet 14 In school

Starting points: Ask the children to draw pictures of what they like doing at school.

Main activity: The children should complete the worksheet and then draw someone taking part in one of their favourite subjects.

Simplified activity: The children should complete the worksheet.

Challenge: Working in pairs, ask the children to decide what the best thing about school is. They should go on to make up a play about an unusual event at school, for example, a dog getting loose and running into the classroom.

Worksheet 15 Choosing

Starting points: Ask the children to tell a partner their three favourite colours. Talk about other favourites.

Main activity: The children should complete the worksheet and then make up lists of their favourite fruits, clothes, animals, games or other favourites.

Simplified activity: The children should complete the worksheet.

Challenge: Ask the children to write a story or poem about a favourite food.

Plenary

- *Talk about what makes something their favourite. It might be the smell, colour or taste.*
- *Take a topic such as food and ask each child to name one food they like and one food they hate. Ask them to explain the reasons behind their decisions.*
- *Discuss the fact that different people have different opinions.*

Friends

 Complete this sheet with a friend.
Working together, which would you choose?
You can only choose one thing from each list.

Games to play

football

skipping

hopscotch

chase

tennis

cricket

We would choose

_____

TV to watch

cartoons

wildlife

cookery

puppets

news

dancing

We would choose

_____

Food to eat

cake

sausages

biscuits

salad

pizza

yoghurt

We would choose

_____

Places to visit

castle

playground

seaside

funfair

museum

shops

We would choose

_____

In school

 Write down the subjects you like best at school. Choose from the list.

Painting	I like …
Writing	_____
Reading	_____
Listening to stories	_____
Number work	_____
Games	_____
Music	_____
Computers	_____

Add some more.

_____

_____

_____

_____

Choosing

 **Choose your favourite thing from each row.
Say why you chose it.**

Meals and more

Background

This unit considers healthy options. It looks at different types of food and also at ways in which people can look after their bodies. The final worksheet in this unit deals with looking after pets.

It is important that young children have the chance to consider different types of food, to understand that some are healthier than others and that they need to be socially responsible individuals. They should also understand the responsibilities of owning a pet.

Learning Objectives

Activities in this unit will allow children to:
- understand that all humans have needs
- understand that we have a certain amount of choice relating to these needs
- consider the needs of their pets.

QCA/Curriculum links: QCA Unit 3 • Worksheet 16 links with English and Science • Worksheet 17 links with English, Science and Art & Design • Worksheet 18 links with English, Science and Art & Design

ACTIVITIES

Worksheet 16 Healthy eating

Starting points: Discuss the children's favourite foods. 'Which healthy foods do you enjoy?'

Main activity: The children should complete the worksheet and then list five other foods that form part of a healthy diet.

Simplified activity: The children should complete the worksheet.

Challenge: The children should make up a menu for a really healthy meal.

Worksheet 17 Looking after our bodies

Starting points: Give the children daily activities such as cleaning teeth to act out.

Main activity: The children should complete the worksheet and then write down some other things they need to do to keep healthy.

Simplified activity: The children should complete the worksheet. There are several correct answers.

Challenge: The children should complete the worksheet and then explain in pictures how to clean teeth.

Worksheet 18 Feeding my pet

Starting points: Ask the children to go through some coloured magazines and cut out pictures of any creatures that could be kept as pets.

Main activity: The children should choose a pet from the worksheet, draw a picture of its home and say why they have chosen this pet.

Simplified activity: The children should complete the worksheet.

Challenge: Ask the children to write a story about a favourite pet, either real or imaginary.

Plenary

- *Discuss with the children how important it is for people to stay healthy. Let them suggest ways in which they can help keep themselves healthy and avoid illness.*
- *Discuss how pets need to be looked after.*

Healthy eating

 Colour in the foods that you might choose as part of a healthy meal

Why?

Looking after our bodies

 Colour in the picture and use the words to fill in the blanks.

I must _____ my hair.

I must _____ my teeth.

I must _____ lots of fruit and vegetables.

I must _____ my hands.

I must keep my feet _____ .

brush   clean   eat   comb   wash

Feeding my pet

 Link each pet to the food it eats.

What else do pets need to keep healthy?

Right and wrong

Background

This unit looks at possible outcomes of a decision and at some examples of right and wrong options. It also considers fairness when making a decision and individuals' ability to make their own decisions whether they are right or wrong. Children need to have experience of decision-making and chances to decide for themselves. The work in this unit can be expanded by providing children with a range of other decision-making exercises.

Learning Objectives

Activities in this section will allow children to:
- recognise the difference between right and wrong
- understand that people do not always make the correct decision
- look at different alternatives.

QCA/Curriculum links: QCA Unit 2 • Worksheet 19 links with English and Art & Design • Worksheet 20 links with English and Mathematics • Worksheet 21 links with English and Design & Technology

ACTIVITIES

Worksheet 19 Right or wrong

Starting points: Talk about right and wrong.

Main activity: The children should complete the worksheet and then pick one picture and draw what might happen next.

Simplified activity: The children should complete the worksheet and then discuss with a partner why they made those choices.

Challenge: The children should complete the worksheet and then discuss with a partner how a friend might be able to help with these decisions.

Worksheet 20 Being fair

Starting points: Split the children into groups of four. Give each group a pile of buttons or counters to share out fairly. Discuss what they would do with an odd number of buttons.

Main activity: The children should complete the worksheet and then go on to share out six biscuits and a pizza between the three friends.

Simplified activity: The children should complete the worksheet and colour it in.

Challenge: The children should complete the worksheet and then write down three reasons why it is important to be fair.

Worksheet 21 Sorting out

Starting points: Talk about why some things go together and others don't.

Main activity: Working in pairs, the children should make up a play to go with one of the rules.

Simplified activity: The children should complete the worksheet and colour it in.

Challenge: The children should produce a poster to go with one of the rules.

Plenary

- *Pick a children's story or nursery rhyme in which characters needed to make a decision, for example, The Three Little Pigs. What did they use to build their homes? Did they all make the correct decision? Discuss their options and the consequences.*
- *Humpty Dumpty, should he have sat on the wall? Why did Little Bo Peep lose her sheep?*

Right or wrong?

 Look at these pictures and answer the questions.

Is it right or wrong for you to **smoke?**

right ☐   wrong ☐

Is it right or wrong to **bully someone?**

right ☐   wrong ☐

Is it right or wrong to **cheat in a game?**

right ☐   wrong ☐

Is it right or wrong to **steal things?**

right ☐   wrong ☐

Why?

30

Being fair

 Divide these sweets fairly between the three friends.

Lewis   Sneha   Poppy

What would you do with any spare sweets?

Sorting out

 Match each picture with the correct rule.

Never talk to strangers.

Put litter in a bin.

Keep away from rivers and ponds.

Cross where it is safe.

Play in a safe place.

32

Problem solving

Background

It is important that young children understand they sometimes need help when there is a problem to be solved. They need to know who the best people are to turn to if a problem occurs. Sometimes they will have to decide for themselves what to do and how to solve a problem. They also need to discuss how they might deal with problems when they are out and about.

Learning Objectives

Activities in this unit will allow children to:
- consider who might be able to help them every day
- think about how they might improve a situation themselves
- imagine a range of situations in which they might need help.

QCA/Curriculum links: QCA Unit 1 • Worksheet 22 links with English and Art & Design • Worksheet 23 links with English • Worksheet 24 links with English and Art & Design

ACTIVITIES

Worksheet 22 Help

Starting points: Make a list of people who help every day at school.

Main activity: The children should complete the worksheet and write the names of the people who help next to their drawings.

Simplified activity: The children should complete the worksheet.

Challenge: The children should complete the worksheet and then write a story or make up a play about how one or more of the people helped them.

Worksheet 23 What would I do?

Starting points: Give the children a selection of situations, such as seeing a younger child crying, and ask what they might do.

Main activity: The children should complete the worksheet and then write down what happens next.

Simplified activity: The children should complete the worksheet.

Challenge: The children should complete the worksheet. On the back they should draw three more situations and discuss possible responses.

Worksheet 24 Out and about

Starting points: Organise a series of role-play exercises involving people in uniform such as police officers and firefighters.

Main activity: The children should complete the worksheet and then write a story to go with their picture.

Simplified activity: The children should complete the worksheet.

Challenge: The children should complete the worksheet and then write down what the person in their picture does as part of their job.

Plenary

- *Ask the children to sit in a circle. Talk about how you should make decisions, using the formula: 'Stop, think, decide.' Make up some more slogans that they could use.*
- *Talk about decisions they have made recently and what influenced their decisions.*

PSHE & Citizenship in Action: Year 2

Help

 Fill this bubble with people who help you every day.

Who is the most important person in the picture? Why?

_____

What would I do?

 Write down what you would do if you saw:

two friends fighting

_____

_____

_____

_____

a lost dog

_____

_____

_____

£5 on the ground

_____

_____

_____

35

Out and about

 Draw a picture of someone in a uniform helping a person with a problem.

9 Needs

Background

This unit looks at what people need to make them happy. It investigates people's responsibility towards wild animals and pets. Animals need the right to behave in a natural way and be attended to if they are sick. Children also need to know how they can protect local wildlife.

Learning Objectives

Activities in this unit will allow children to:
- appreciate that people need to be both healthy and happy
- understand that people have responsibilities to domestic and wild animals
- understand that people sometimes need to provide for wild creatures.

QCA/Curriculum links: QCA Unit 3 • Worksheet 25 links with English and Music • Worksheet 26 links with English, Science and Art & Design • Worksheet 27 links with English and ICT

ACTIVITIES

Worksheet 25 How can we be happy?

Starting points: Ask for favourite jokes. Write them down. Discuss what makes people laugh.

Main activity: The children should complete the worksheet and then write down and draw what might make someone happy.

Simplified activity: The children should complete the worksheet.

Challenge: The children should complete the worksheet and then make up extra verses to 'If You're Happy and You Know It'.

Worksheet 26 Wildlife around the school

Starting points: List rules to remember when looking after animals or fish.

Main activity: The children should write a sentence to go with each of their drawings.

Simplified activity: The children should complete the worksheet.

Challenge: The children should complete the worksheet and then list things they could do to help creatures and plants around the school.

Worksheet 27 How can we help?

Starting points: Make a list of questions the children could ask an invited speaker.

Main activity: The children should complete the worksheet and then address an envelope.

Simplified activity: The children should complete the worksheet and decorate their letter.

Challenge: The children should complete the worksheet and then use ICT to find out which organisations help pets and wild animals locally.

Plenary

- *Discuss with the children ways in which they can help their pets if they become sick and how they can support wildlife around the school.*
- *If any of the children have had sick pets, ask them to tell the others what happened. Who helped them? How?*

How can we be happy?

 Complete these words.

_____ appy   _____ mile

_____ olly   _____ un

_____ ump   _____ augh

> happy   fun   jolly   laugh   jump   smile

Put each word into a sentence.

_____

_____

_____

_____

_____

Wildlife around the school

 Draw pictures of some of the wildlife you might find around your school.

minibeast

bird

animal

plant

How can we help?

 Write a letter to a local wildlife group asking them to come to talk to you.

Dear

(10) Safety

Background

It is important that people keep their possessions safe. Children may bring things to school that are very similar, for example, pencil cases and bags. Sometimes these things get muddled up or go missing. It is important that children know that things sometimes get lost but sometimes they are taken by someone else. A set of class rules often helps. Personal safety is another issue that should be discussed and children need to be aware that people of all ages can be at risk.

Learning Objectives

Activities in this unit will allow children to:
- develop ways of keeping their property safe
- talk about ways in which they can keep themselves safe
- develop skills to keep themselves safe.

QCA/Curriculum links: QCA Unit 4 • Worksheet 28 links with English and Art & Design • Worksheet 29 links with English and Design & Technology • Worksheet 30 links with English and Design & Technology

ACTIVITIES

Worksheet 28 — Protecting ourselves

Starting points: Discuss why it is important to be sensible when out playing.

Main activity: The children should complete the worksheet and then draw pictures of people who might be able to help children in difficulty.

Simplified activity: The children should complete the worksheet.

Challenge: The children should complete the worksheet and then make up a play about someone who might be at risk.

Worksheet 29 — Keeping our things safe

Starting points: Make some labels that could be used to help keep the children's things safe.

Main activity: The children should complete the worksheet and then draw one item, showing what could be written on it to prevent it going missing.

Simplified activity: The children should complete the worksheet.

Challenge: The children should complete the worksheet and list on the back ways in which personal things can be protected when they are not at school.

Worksheet 30 — The safety code

Starting points: Take a walk around the school and make up some safety rules.

Main activity: The children should complete the worksheet and produce a set of pictures to go with the rules.

Simplified activity: The children should complete the worksheet.

Challenge: The children should complete the worksheet and then make up a set of safety rules for use outside school.

Plenary

- *Talk about how the children can protect their property.*
- *Discuss how things go missing. How can they, as a group, prevent this from happening?*
- *Ask the children to produce a class safety code for keeping themselves safe.*

PSHE & Citizenship in Action: Year 2

Protecting ourselves

What should the twins do if...

1 They get lost.

_____

2 They are walking home.

_____

3 A stranger talks to them.

_____

4 They have to cross the road.

_____

5 They see a friend playing near a railway line.

_____

Who can you ask for help?

_____

_____

Complete these words.

D __ nger   H __ lp   P __ l __ ce   Frien __

Keeping our things safe

 Put a tick by the things you own.

☐	pen	☐	ruler	☐	rubber
☐	pencil	☐	comb	☐	hat
☐	bag	☐	coat	☐	lunchbox

How can you keep these things safe?

■ _____

■ _____

■ _____

Why do things go missing?

■ _____

■ _____

■ _____

What can you do if something goes missing?

■ _____

■ _____

■ _____

■ _____

The safety code

Write down a set of rules that will help keep things safe at school

_____

_____

_____

_____

_____

_____

_____

_____

_____

Which is the most important rule? Why?

_____

_____

People who help us

Background

This unit examines in more detail jobs carried out by people who help the public. How do these people support and help the community? The children have the opportunity to name the parts of a police officer's uniform. They should be able to know what to do in an emergency and how to recognise different uniforms. Finally, they have the chance to investigate things they can do to remain safe.

Learning Objectives

Activities in this unit will allow children to:
- understand more fully how certain people can help them and the community
- recognise different uniforms
- understand how they might keep themselves safe in a variety of situations.

QCA/Curriculum links: QCA Unit 4 • Worksheet 31 links with English and Art & Design • Worksheet 32 links with English, Design & Technology and Art & Design • Worksheet 33 links with English and Art & Design

ACTIVITIES

Worksheet 31   What do they do?

Starting points: Prepare a set of job cards. Ask children to explain what each job involves.

Main activity: The children should complete the worksheet and then list some of the other jobs that are carried out by these people.

Simplified activity: The children should complete the worksheet.

Challenge: The children should complete the worksheet and then draw some of the other people who help them and list what they do.

Worksheet 32   Uniforms

Starting points: Make a list of people who wear uniforms.

Main activity: The children should complete the worksheet and then list people they might meet who wear uniforms.

Simplified activity: The children should complete the worksheet and colour the picture.

Challenge: The children should complete the worksheet and then draw the uniforms of a fire fighter and a nurse, naming the different parts.

Worksheet 33   Keeping safe

Starting points: Discuss the importance of safety in the classroom.

Main activity: The children should complete the worksheet and then draw a picture to go with each example showing what happened next.

Simplified activity: The children should complete the worksheet and colour in the pictures.

Challenge: The children should make up a play about someone who did not follow a safety rule.

Plenary

- *Talk about the importance of knowing what to do in different situations.*
- *Invite the local community police officer to come in to talk about a variety of safety issues and ways in which the children can be more assertive when they are outside school.*

What do they do?

 What do these people do? Match them up with the sentences below.

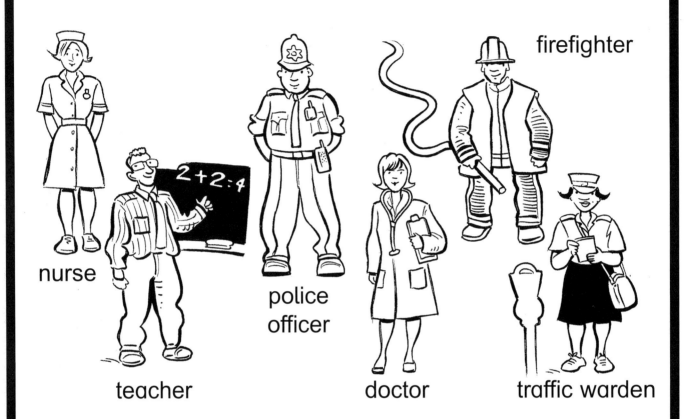

firefighter

nurse

police officer

teacher

doctor

traffic warden

Finds out why someone is sick. _____

Teaches children lots of things. _____

Looks after sick people. _____

Checks where people park. _____

Fights crime. _____

Prevents and puts out fires _____

Someone else who helps us is …

_____

46

Uniforms

 Label this police officer's uniform.

number

pen

boots

stick

hat

notebook

shirt

handcuffs

Keeping safe

 What might happen next?

_____

_____

_____

_____

_____

_____

_____

_____

_____

_____

_____

_____

What could you do to help?

(12) Police

Background

The police have a number of different roles, including crime prevention. They can help people to look after their property and advise people about the best ways of protecting themselves. Children can be fully involved in this by looking after their bicycles, making sure their home is secure before they leave it and being socially aware when they are out and about.

Learning Objectives

Activities in this unit will allow children to:
- learn how best to protect their property
- understand how important it is to become part of the community
- be more socially responsible.

QCA/Curriculum links: QCA Unit 4 • Worksheet 34 links with English and Design & Technology • Worksheet 35 links with English, Music, Design & Technology and Art & Design • Worksheet 36 links with English

ACTIVITIES

Worksheet 34 Protecting my bike

Starting points: Bring in a bicycle and talk about how it works and how to make it safe.

Main activity: The children should complete the worksheet and then write on the back what to do if a bike is stolen.

Simplified activity: The children should complete the worksheet.

Challenge: The children should complete the worksheet and then list ways the police might protect children's bicycles.

Worksheet 35 Our home

Starting points: Sing 'London's Burning'. Discuss how to protect homes from fire.

Main activity: The children should complete the worksheet and then list on the back five ways in which people might protect their homes.

Simplified activity: The children should complete the worksheet.

Challenge: The children should complete the worksheet and then draw on the back some of the things that can be used to protect a home, for example, burglar alarm, dog or bars.

Worksheet 36 Where we live

Starting points: Talk about where the children live. What do they think of their home?

Main activity: The children should complete the worksheet and then discuss with a partner which home would be the easiest to protect and why.

Simplified activity: The children should complete the worksheet.

Challenge: The children should complete the worksheet and then discuss with a partner how the area around their own home could be made safer.

Plenary

- *Talk about ways in which property can be protected.*
- *Discuss why a burglar alarm or a dog might be a good idea.*
- *Talk about the importance of not only looking after your own home and property but also the local area. Who can help with this?*

PSHE & Citizenship in Action: Year 2

Protecting my bike

 Make a list of ways of protecting your bike.

- _____
- _____
- _____
- _____
- _____
- _____

Tick the best places to leave your bike.

☐ In a dark corner   ☐ At home

☐ By a street light   ☐ Behind a tree

☐ Chained to a bike stand   ☐ With a friend

Our home

 **What would you do before you
left this house? Why?**

_____

_____

_____

_____

_____

How do you make sure your home is safe?

_____

_____

Where we live

 Where would you like to live? Why?
Colour in your favourite place below.

How could you protect it?

Similarities and differences

Background

Children need to know that all people have similarities and differences and that there are other countries and other people around the world. Some children in the class may have relatives elsewhere in the world or may have been on holiday to other countries. Ask them to talk about where they have been and the experiences they had.

Learning Objectives

Activities in this unit will allow children to:
- learn about other countries
- understand that everyone is different
- reflect on the differences between countries around the world.

QCA/Curriculum links: QCA Unit 5 • Worksheet 37 links with English, ICT and Geography • Worksheet 38 links with English and Geography • Worksheet 39 links with English, Geography and PE

ACTIVITIES

Worksheet 37 Going abroad

Starting points: Ask the children to bring in postcards. Talk about the pictures and places.

Main activity: The children should complete the worksheet and then make a list of some of the countries children in the class have been to.

Simplified activity: The children should complete the worksheet.

Challenge: The children should complete the worksheet and then pick one country and use books and ICT to find out more about it.

Worksheet 38 Togetherness

Starting points: Collect pictures of cities and the countryside. Discuss similarities and differences between them.

Main activity: The children should complete the worksheet and then write a short story about the two friends.

Simplified activity: The children should complete the worksheet.

Challenge: The children should complete the worksheet and then discuss with a partner how this place is different from where they live.

Worksheet 39 Having fun

Starting points: Play a game the children enjoy. Discuss why they like playing it.

Main activity: The children should complete the worksheet and then list other games which the children in the picture could play together.

Simplified activity: The children should complete the worksheet.

Challenge: The children should complete the worksheet and then work with a partner to make up a game they could play using a ball or ball and bat.

Plenary

- *Ask the children to imagine that they live somewhere else. Ask them to describe what it might be like to live there. How would it be different from where they live now?*
- *Ask the children to cut some pictures of different places from magazines and then draw a picture of themselves to add to the pictures.*

PSHE & Citizenship in Action: Year 2

Going abroad

 Chloe and Ben live in a city.
They go on holiday to Spain. Talk to your partner about how the two places are different.

Colour the pictures.

Togetherness

 Here are two friends.
They live in a village in Sudan.
What are they saying to each other?
Fill in the bubbles.
Now finish the picture.

Having fun

 What games do these friends like to play?
Draw them playing four different games.

(14) Connections

Background

Lots of things that people buy and eat in this country come from abroad. In some cases, raw materials from abroad are used to produce new products. Many vegetables and fruits that are eaten in the UK also come from overseas. Children need to know the connection between these goods and understand that they live in an interdependent world.

Learning Objectives

Activities in this unit will allow children to:
- understand that lots of things they eat and use come from overseas
- begin to collect evidence to show that they live in an interdependent world.
- understand that raw materials such as rubber, wood and cotton often come from another country.

QCA/Curriculum links: QCA Unit 5 • Worksheet 40 links with English and Science • Worksheet 41 links with English, Geography and Art & Design• Worksheet 42 links with English and Geography

ACTIVITIES

Worksheet 40 Connections

Starting points: Make a set of cards showing things that are connected. Ask the children to pair them up.

Main activity: The children should complete the worksheet and then add to the lists of items and raw materials shown.

Simplified activity: Help the children to complete the worksheet. Ask them to colour the pictures.

Challenge: The children should complete the worksheet and then draw a diagram showing how something is made.

Worksheet 41 Where did it come from?

Starting points: Visit a supermarket or shop. Investigate where the products come from.

Main activity: The children should complete the worksheet and then investigate how many things they are wearing come from another country.

Simplified activity: The children should complete the worksheet.

Challenge: The children should complete the worksheet and then draw some fruit and vegetables that grow abroad.

Worksheet 42 Different places

Starting points: Show the children a map of the world and talk about different parts of it.

Main activity: The children should complete the worksheet and then list things children in the class have for breakfast and where they come from.

Simplified activity: The children should complete the worksheet and find the places on a map.

Challenge: The children should complete the worksheet and then produce a map showing where goods and food come from.

Plenary

- *Bring in some different types of vegetable and fruit. Pass each one round a circle of children and ask if they think it was grown in this country or abroad. Talk about how each grows.*

Connections

 Look at the objects on the left. Match them up with the thing they are made from.

Where did it come from?

 Lots of things we use come from other countries. Colour in green things that probably come from another country.

Different places

 Look at the things in the picture.
Where do you think they come from? Match
the things with the places.

(15) Our school

Background

School plays an important part in every child's life and this unit has been designed to help them become more involved. Concentrating on the school site, it looks at the building and the grounds and examines ways in which these might be improved. The children may prefer to concentrate on the exterior of the building where they may have more influence on what is carried out.

Learning Objectives

Activities in this unit will allow children to:
- contribute to the life of the school
- realise that money comes from different places
- be able to take part in discussions with others.

QCA/Curriculum links: QCA Unit 6 • Worksheet 43 links with English, Design & Technology, Geography and Art & Design • Worksheet 44 links with English, Design & Technology, Geography, Art & Design and Music • Worksheet 45 links with English and Music

ACTIVITIES

Worksheet 43   Improvements

Starting points: Talk about improvements that might be made to the school building.

Main activity: The children should complete the worksheet and discuss who might be able to help with any changes.

Simplified activity: The children should complete the worksheet.

Challenge: The children should complete the worksheet and then draw some plans showing how things might look after the proposed changes.

Worksheet 44   My school

Starting points: Discuss why the children like coming to school. Make up your own school song based on the tune of 'Old Macdonald.'

Main activity: The children should complete the worksheet and then list things children in the class like and dislike about the school and its grounds.

Simplified activity: The children should complete the worksheet.

Challenge: The children should complete the worksheet and then construct a model of what the school and grounds might look like after the proposed change.

Worksheet 45   Raising money

Starting points: Talk about how money raised voluntarily could be used for good causes.

Main activity: The children should complete the worksheet and then make up a song or jingle to advertise one event.

Simplified activity: The children should complete the worksheet.

Challenge: The children should complete the worksheet and then discuss, in small groups, what the class could do to help raise money.

Plenary

- *After discussing their opinions and suggestions for improvements, ask a number of people to come in to talk about how the school grounds might be improved.*
- *Discuss how the children might raise money for one improvement.*

Improvements

 Write down or draw some of the ways
you could improve your school.

The playground

The classroom

The gardens or entrance

My school

 Underline two changes you would like to see in your school.

- More space in the playground

- Climbing frame in the playground

- More tables in the classroom

- New computers

- Bigger hall

- Better toilets

- More plants and flowers outside

- New swimming pool

Draw a picture of one of the improvements.

Raising money

 How could you raise money to help pay for changes in your school?
Use the word search to find the answers.

F	U	N	R	U	N	D	L
P	Z	O	Q	R	V	A	S
W	F	A	I	R	P	B	H
F	G	N	V	E	N	K	S
E	J	D	A	N	C	E	A
T	V	P	T	O	I	J	L
E	B	R	E	S	W	Q	E
L	K	T	Z	X	G	J	M

Dance   Fete   Sale   Fun run   Fair